PADDINGTON'S JAR OF JOKES

Paddington's Jar of Jokes

written by Michael Bond
illustrated by Tony Kenyon

Carnival
An Imprint of HarperCollins*Publishers*

Paddington's Jar of Jokes was first
published by Carnival in 1992.

Carnival is an imprint of
HarperCollins Publishers Ltd
of 77/85 Fulham Palace Road,
Hammersmith, London W6 8JB

ISBN 0 00 674309 9

Printed and bound in Great Britain by
HarperCollins Manufacturing, Glasgow

Knock knock!
Who's there?
Paddington.
Paddington who?

Paddington Brown from Darkest Peru
and I'm afraid I can't reach the bell...

Every time I hear a new joke I write it in my scrap book. My friend, Mr Gruber, suggested I ought to make a collection of them.

So that's what I've done.

And here it is...

Food Funnies

Eating is a serious business, which is probably why there are so many "Waiter, there's a fly in my soup!" jokes.

Jonathan thinks that if all the flies stood on top of each other they would make a tremendous splash when they fell in. But I think it's the same fly each time. It just happens to be very fond of soup!

CUSTOMER: Waiter, I would like some fish.
WAITER: Come this way, Sir. I'll find you a plaice...

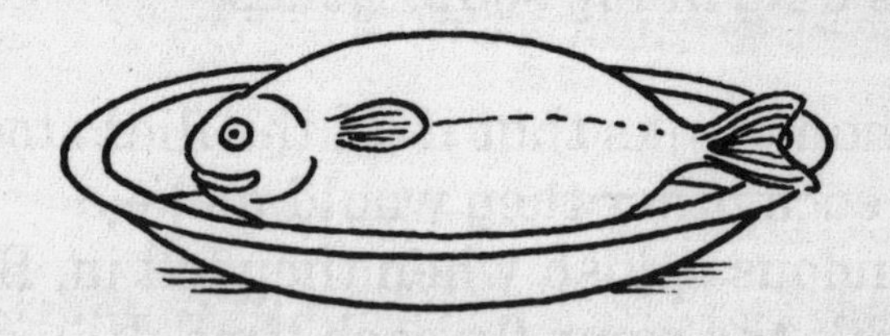

MR CURRY: Waiter! There's a fly in my soup.
WAITER: They don't care what they eat, do they, Sir?

MR CURRY: Now I've found a spider.
WAITER: He's probably after the fly. Anyway, he won't live long in that stuff!

MR CURRY: And there are some insects nibbling my lettuce.
WAITER: Don't worry, Sir. They have very small appetites.

MR CURRY: Waiter, what is this dish?
WAITER: It's bean soup, Sir.
MR CURRY: I don't care what it's been.
I want to know what it is now!

CUSTOMER: Waiter – this egg tastes off.
WAITER: Don't blame me, Sir. I only laid the table.

CUSTOMER: Waiter, you may not believe this but I've found a button in my soup.
WAITER: Thank you very much, Madam. I wondered where it had gone.

CUSTOMER: Waiter, this lobster has only one claw.

WAITER: I'm afraid it got into a fight with another lobster, Sir.

CUSTOMER: Well, would you please bring me the winner?

MR CURRY: Waiter, you've got your thumb on my steak.

WAITER: I know, Sir. I didn't want it to fall on the floor again.

MR CURRY: Waiter, this steak is tough. Try some and see what you think.
WAITER: It tastes quite tender to me, Sir.
MR CURRY: That's the bit I've been chewing for the past ten minutes.

CUSTOMER: Waiter, does the pianist do requests?
WAITER: Yes, Sir.
CUSTOMER: Well, would you ask him to go somewhere else and play?

MR CURRY: Waiter, this meal is disgusting. I would like to see the chef.

WAITER: You're not the only one, Sir. I'll tell him as soon as he gets back from lunch.

MR CURRY: In that case, call the manager. I can't eat this mess.

WAITER: I doubt if he'll eat it either, Sir.

CUSTOMER: Waiter! This coffee tastes like mud.

WAITER: I'm not surprised, Madam. It was ground only a moment or so ago.

Waiter, please call me a taxi.
Very well, Sir. You're a taxi.

Creature Chuckles

It probably won't surprise you to hear that I've a big collection of animal jokes. Some of them were handed down to me by my Uncle in Darkest Peru.

Jonathan thinks he was probably glad to get rid of them...

What do you call an escaped gorilla?
Sir!

What weighs over a ton and wears a bead necklace?
A hippy-potamus.

What do you get if you cross a giraffe with a dog?
An animal that barks at low flying aircraft.

What goes "wuff wuff, tick tick"?
A watch dog.

PADDINGTON: Mr Gruber told me they've had trouble at the Flea Circus.
JUDY: Really? What happened?
PADDINGTON: A dog stole the show.

What do you get if you cross a jeep with a dog?
A land rover.

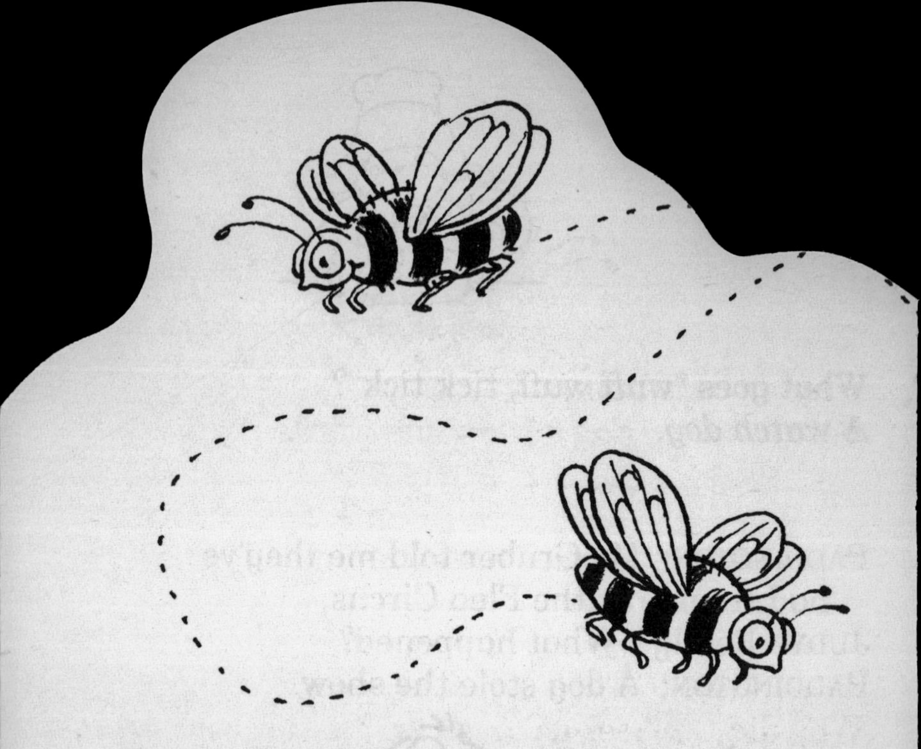

Why can leopards never escape from a safari park?
Because they are always spotted.

What do you do for a budgie on its birthday?
Take it out for a tweet.

What succeeds?
A budgie without any teeth.

How do you milk a porcupine?
Very carefully!

Why do bees hum?
Because they don't know the words.

Where might you see bees forming a queue?
At a buzz stop.

Why did the bees go on strike?
Because they wanted more honey and shorter flowers.

Where do baby gorillas sleep?
In apricots.

What is smaller than a fly's mouth?
Whatever goes into it.

What did the pony say when he coughed?
Excuse me. I'm a little hoarse.

What did the Spanish farmer say to his hen?
Olé!

Why did the chicken run on to the
football pitch?
Because the referee called a foul.

Library Laughs

I like a good book. I read one the other day all about life in a glue factory. I couldn't put it down! Then there was one called "Knitting for Pleasure". It had me in stitches!

DESERT JOURNEY
by Rhoda Camel
HOW TO PLAY THE PIANO
by Ivor E. Keys
MY LIFE OF CRIME
by Robin Banks
YOUR MONEY OR YOUR LIFE
by Ann Dover
TIME FOR SCHOOL
by R. U. Upjohn
KEEP FIT FOR ALL
by Horace Zontalbars

Doctor Doctor!

I never knew what a funny place hospitals could be until the day when the Browns' next-door neighbour, Mr Curry had to go into hospital with a suspected broken leg. He'd slipped on one of my marmalade sandwiches, but that's another story! Mr Curry is so mean he asked me to take him a fork in case anyone in the ward wanted to use his sugar.

When I went to visit him, the doctors mistook me for a visiting surgeon! I kept overhearing such funny things while I was looking for Mr Curry. Jonathan said I was in stitches for weeks afterwards...

PATIENT: Doctor, I don't know what's wrong but people keep ignoring me.
DOCTOR: Next please!

PATIENT: Doctor, I feel like a dog.
DOCTOR: Lie down on the bed and tell me all about it.
PATIENT: I can't. I'm not allowed on the furniture.

MR CURRY: Doctor, I think I'm shrinking.
DOCTOR: Well, you'll just have to be a little patient.

PATIENT: Doctor, I keep wanting to cover myself with gold paint.
DOCTOR: You must be suffering from a gilt complex.

DOCTOR: You know, you really ought to have your eyes checked.
PATIENT: I'm quite happy keeping them blue, thank you.

PATIENT: Doctor – please help me. I can't remember anything for more than a second.
DOCTOR: How long has this been going on for?
PATIENT: How long has what been going on for?

PATIENT: Doctor, I keep seeing double.
DOCTOR: Lie down on that bed and I'll examine you.
PATIENT: Er – which bed?

PATIENT: Doctor, I keep seeing green and yellow spots.
DOCTOR: Have you seen an optician?
PATIENT: No, only green and yellow spots.

VISITOR: Doctor, come quickly! My baby's swallowed a pen.

DOCTOR: I'll come in two minutes. What are you doing in the mean time?

VISITOR: Using a pencil.

It may not be true,
That in Darkest Peru
I was a poet,
And didn't know it.

But at various times,
I've collected some rhymes,
(Mostly they're terse,
Or go from bad to verse!)

There was a young bear from Peru,
Whose coat was all woolly and blue.
When he undid his toggles
He caused a few boggles
Not to mention a "tut tut" or two.

There was a young bear cub from Cheadle,
Who sat down in church on a needle.
Though deeply imbedded
It was luckily threaded
So he had it removed by the Beadle.

There was a young bear cub from Kent,
Whose nose was all battered and bent.
One day he arose
And followed his nose
But no one knew which way he went.

There was a young bear from Utrecht,
Who twisted his paws round his neck.
Like a fool he forgot
How to undo the knot
And now he's an absolute wreck.

There was a young bear from Nepal,
Who was asked to a fancy dress ball.
He decided to risk it
And go as a biscuit,
But the rumba put paid to it all.

An unlucky young bear cub from Leeds,
By mistake ate a packet of seeds.
Within half an hour
His face was in flower
And his head was all covered with weeds.

Classroom Chortles

The day I went to school felt very strange. My Aunt Lucy taught me all she knew before I emigrated from Darkest Peru, so I didn't really see the need for me to go.

Judy says it wasn't long before the school felt the same way...

TEACHER: Paddington, you're late. You should have been here at 9 o'clock.

PADDINGTON: Oh dear. What happened?

PADDINGTON: Oh good. It's sums first. Bears are good at sums.

TEACHER: Is that so? Well, we'll see about that. Tell me who invented vulgar fractions.

PADDINGTON: Henry the Eighth.

TEACHER: If you had a pile of 200 beans and you ate 175, what would you have?

PADDINGTON: Indigestion.

TEACHER: How many beans make five?
PADDINGTON: Mr Gruber says it depends if you are buying or selling.

TEACHER: If you opened your suitcase and found you had £20 inside, then you looked inside the secret compartment and found you had another £15, what would you have?

PADDINGTON: Someone else's suitcase.

TEACHER: If there were 10 flies in a row and you killed one with a fly swat, how many would you have left?

PADDINGTON: None. The rest would have flown away.

TEACHER: If you lent your next door neighbour £5 and he paid you back at the rate of £1 per month, how long would it be before you got all of your money back?
PADDINGTON: Years and years.
TEACHER: I'm afraid you don't know your arithmetic after all, Paddington.
PADDINGTON: I'm afraid you don't know our neighbour – Mr Curry – Miss.

TEACHER: I think we've had enough mathematics for today. Let's move on to science. Hands up anyone who can tell me about nitrates.

PADDINGTON: Miss! They're cheaper than day rates.

TEACHER: Perhaps you can tell me what is used to conduct electricity.

PADDINGTON: Why...er...

TEACHER: Very good. Wire.

TEACHER: What is the difference between oxygen and nitrogen?

PADDINGTON: Well, we breathe oxygen during the day and nitrogen during the night.

Knock knock!
Who's there?
Cook.
Cook who?
That's the first cuckoo
I've heard in ages!

Knock knock!
Who's there?
Tish.
Tish who?
Bless you!

Knock knock!
Who's there?
Shirley.
Shirley who?
Shirley I've no need
to tell you!

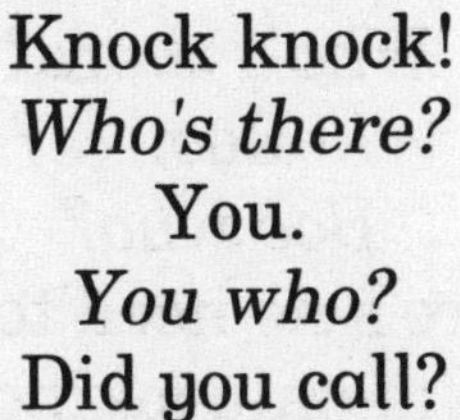

Knock knock!
Who's there?
You.
You who?
Did you call?

Knock knock!
Who's there?
Arthur.
Arthur who?
Are there any more
at home like you?

Knock knock!
Who's there?
Boo.
Boo who?
There's no need to cry.
I'm only joking.

HOME DECORATING
by Polly Filla

AT THE ELEVENTH HOUR
by Justin Time

THE DOG'S DINNER
by Nora Bone

HOW TO GET THERE IN THE END
by Percy Vere

UNUSUAL PETS
by Terry Dactyl
MY LIFE AS A CARPET FITTER
by Walter Wall
COLD CUTS AND SALADS
by Della Cattessen

Assorted Gems

What game do monsters play?
Swallow My Leader

What do you call a man who looks down in the mouth?
A dentist.

Which paw should you stir your cocoa with – your left or your right?
Neither. You should use a spoon.

CINEMA MANAGER: That's the third time you've been in today, and you haven't even seen the film. Is there something wrong?

MAN: I'll say. Every time I go inside, a girl with a torch comes and tears my ticket in two.

How could you cut the sea in half?
With a sea-saw!

What is orange and white and can travel at over one hundred miles an hour?
A train driver's marmalade sandwich.

PADDINGTON: Is this river good for fish?
FISHERMAN: It must be. None of them want to leave!

MR BROWN: This suit is tighter than my skin.
TAILOR: That's impossible, Sir.
MR BROWN: Well, I can sit down in my skin!

Why wouldn't the barber shave the man with a wooden leg?
Because he preferred to use a razor.

Hickory dickory dock
Three mice ran up the clock.
The clock struck one...
But the other two managed to escape.

What do you buy a man who suffers from water on the knee?
A pair of drainpipe trousers.

PADDINGTON: The best present I ever had was a mouth organ. Mr Brown gave me 10 pence every week not to play it.

What happened when the bell fell in
the water?
It got wringing wet.

How did the baker get an electric shock?
*He stood on a bun and a currant ran up
his leg!*

What can be right but never wrong?
An angle.

How did Mr Curry fall off a 30 metre ladder
and not get hurt?
He fell off the bottom rung.

What's yellow and stupid?
Very thick custard.

Dotty Doctors!

I had a very strange dream the other night. I think it stems from the time I went to see Mr Curry in hospital. Anyway, in my dream I was the patient and the doctor looked very much like Mr Curry...

PADDINGTON: Doctor, I feel like a billiard ball.
DR CURRY: In that case, go to the front of the queue!

PADDINGTON: Doctor, my fur is falling out. Can you give me something to keep it in?
DR CURRY: How about this carrier bag.

PADDINGTON: Doctor, can you suggest a cure for sleep-walking?
DR CURRY: Try sprinkling these tin tacks on the floor every night before you go to bed.

PADDINGTON: Doctor, I think I've just swallowed a roll of film.
DR CURRY: Don't worry. We'll see how it develops.

DR CURRY: You've broken your arm in two places. I'm afraid it will have to be in plaster for at least six weeks.
PADDINGTON: Oh dear. Shall I be able to play the violin when it comes off?
DR CURRY: I see no reason why not.
PADDINGTON: Oh good. I couldn't before.

PADDINGTON: Doctor, I think I'm a pack of cards.
DR CURRY: Wait outside. I'll deal with you later.

PADDINGTON: Doctor, I feel as sick as a dog.
DR CURRY: In that case I advise you to see a vet!

DR CURRY: Open wide, please... Goodness! You need a dentist. That's the biggest cavity I've ever seen. That's the biggest cavity I've ever seen.

PADDINGTON: There's no need to go on. I heard you the first time.

DR CURRY: That wasn't me. It was the echo.

I must admit, I was rather relieved to wake up...

Potty Pets and
Batty Beasts

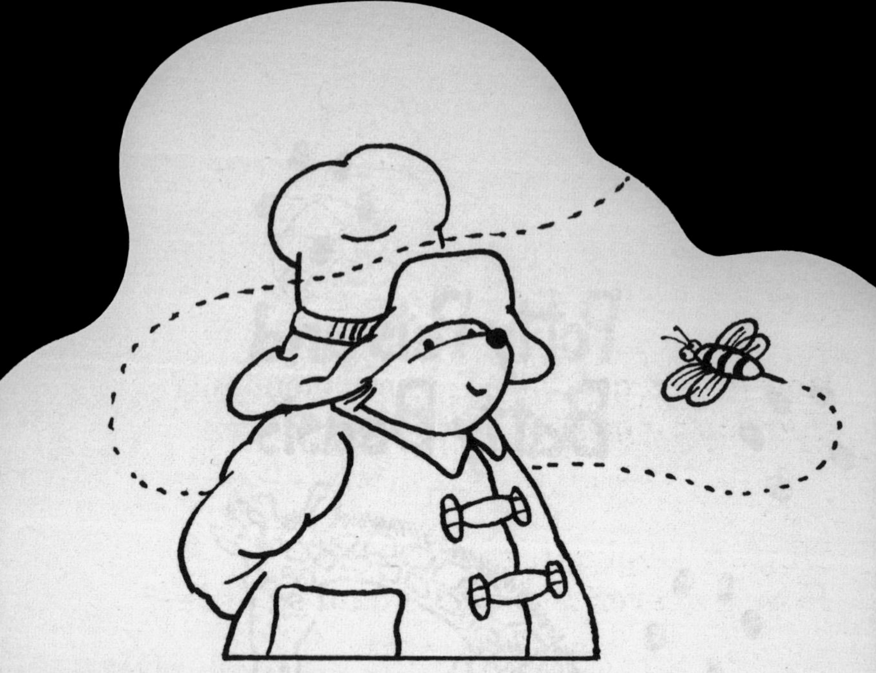

PADDINGTON: Excuse me. I'd like to buy a wasp, please.

PETSHOP OWNER: I'm afraid we don't sell wasps, Sir.

PADDINGTON: Well, you've got one in the window.

What did the police do when the hare escaped from a pet shop?
They combed the area.

How do you stop a dog from barking in the back seat of a car?
Put him in the front.

How do you get down from an elephant?
You don't – you get down from a duck.

Why are elephants so wrinkled?
Have you ever tried ironing an elephant?

If you saw an elephant sitting on your television, what time would it be?
Time to get a new television.

What do you get if you cross an elephant with a mouse?
Very big holes in the skirting board.

What do you get if you cross an elephant with a kangaroo?
Very big holes all over Australia.

JUDY: What do you get if you cross a gorilla with a hyena?
PADDINGTON: I don't know.
JUDY: Neither do I, but when it laughs you'd better join in!

JONATHAN: OK, what do you get if you cross a crocodile with a rose?
PADDINGTON: I don't know that either, but I wouldn't want to smell it!

Which animal is it dangerous to play cards with?
A cheetah!

What is the difference between a lion and a banana?
Try peeling a lion – you'll soon find out.

What did the beaver say to the tree?
It's been nice gnawing you.

PADDINGTON: Do you have any kittens half price?
PETSHOP OWNER: No, but I have a canary going cheap.
PADDINGTON: It doesn't look very good.
PETSHOP OWNER: That's because it's been knocked down.

What steps do you take if you meet an escaped lion?
Long ones.

Why is it difficult to talk when there are goats around?
Because they keep butting in.

What do you do with a seasick gorilla?
Stand clear!

What did the baby hedgehog say when it backed into a cactus?
Hello mum!

What do you get if you cross a skunk with an owl?
A bird that stinks but doesn't give a hoot.

What's yellow and red, with a green tongue and bloodshot eyes?
I don't know.
Neither do I, but I've just seen one crawl up your trouser leg...

Where do the biggest gorillas sleep?
Anywhere they feel like!

More Classroom Chortles

I think bears must be good at lessons. I only went to school for one day, but the teacher said she never wanted to see me again!

TEACHER: All right, Paddington? Let's see what you're like on General Knowledge. Where did King John sign the Magna Carta?

PADDINGTON: At the bottom of the page, Miss.

TEACHER: What was the first thing Henry V did when he came to the throne?

PADDINGTON: He sat down.

TEACHER: Name the four seasons.

PADDINGTON: Mustard, pepper, salt and vinegar.

TEACHER: What comes after the letter A?
PADDINGTON: The rest of the alphabet.

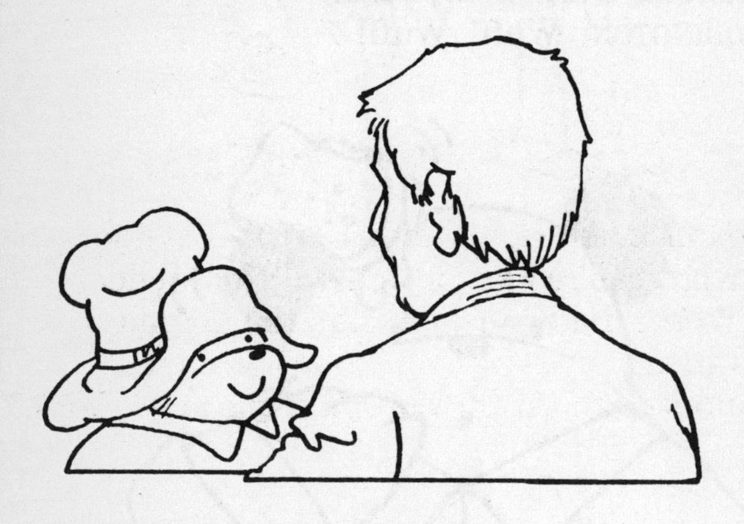

TEACHER: How do you spell wrong?
PADDINGTON: R, O, N, G.
TEACHER: That's wrong!
PADDINGTON: Thank you, Sir.

TEACHER: Where were potatoes first found?
PADDINGTON: In the ground.

TEACHER: What is the outside of a tree called?
PADDINGTON: I don't know, Miss.
TEACHER: Bark, bear, bark!
PADDINGTON: Wuff! Wuff!

TEACHER: Er... why do you have a marmalade sandwich behind your ear?
PADDINGTON: What? Oh dear – I must have eaten my pencil!

What a pity the dinner bell rang just then. I was doing so well! But I heard more new jokes in the canteen.

PUPIL: Please can I have some burnt sausages, lumpy mashed potatoes and two slices of gravy?

DINNER LADY: I couldn't possibly give you anything like that!

PUPIL: I don't see why not. You did yesterday.

BOY AT THE NEXT TABLE: My father can hold up a car with one hand.
PADDINGTON: He must be very strong!
BOY: No. He's a policeman.

BOY: We had a film with our school dinner yesterday.
PADDINGTON: That must have been nice for you.
BOY: No it wasn't. It was on the gravy!

BOY: I bet I can make you say black.
GIRL: I bet you can't.
BOY: What are the colours of the Union Jack?
GIRL: Red, white and blue.
BOY: There you are!
GIRL: But I didn't say black.
BOY: You have now!

SCHOOL GIRL: What is frozen water?
PADDINGTON: Iced water.
GIRL: What is frozen cream?
PADDINGTON: Iced cream.
GIRL: What is frozen ink?
PADDINGTON: Iced ink.
GIRL: It's time you had a bath, then!

How do you start a pudding race?
Say go!

How do you start a jelly race?
Get set!

Why is a football pitch often wet?
The players do a lot of dribbling.

Last Laughs from the Library

DO IT YOURSELF
by Andy Gadget
THE WIND OF CHANGE
by Gail Force
MUSTN'T GRUMBLE
by Mona Lott

More Assorted Gems

Do you know the story about the empty marmalade jar?
There's nothing in it.

Why couldn't the skeleton go to the ball?
Because he had no body to dance with.

Where in the world does Friday come before Thursday?
In a dictionary.

How do you make gold soup?
Put 24 carrots in it.

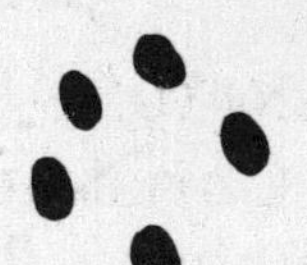

Where is Felixstowe?
At the end of his foot.

What has antlers and eats cheese?
Mickey Moose.

Did you hear about the two burglars who stole a calendar?
They each got six months.

PADDINGTON: I'm going to give you a vase for Christmas, Mrs Brown.
MRS BROWN: That's very kind of you, Paddington, but I already have one.
PADDINGTON: No you haven't. I'm afraid I just dropped it.

What goes zzub zzub?
A bee flying backwards.

Why did the old lady have her hair in a bun?
Because she had her nose in a hamburger.

Why are tall people lazier than short people?
Because they are longer in bed.

Why don't your handkerchief and your nose like each other?
Because they always come to blows when they meet.

Why don't many people play the harp?
Because it takes a lot of pluck.

What is very tall and goes "muf of if eef"?
A giant walking backwards.

Why is honey very expensive in Brazil?
Because there is only one B in Brazil.

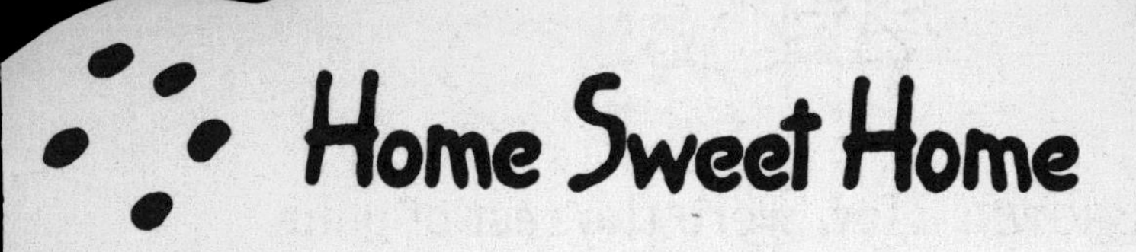

Home Sweet Home

MR BROWN: What did you do at school today, Paddington?

PADDINGTON: We had maths and I only got one sum out of twenty wrong.

MR BROWN: That's good. The teacher must have been very pleased with you.

PADDINGTON: Not really. I couldn't do the other nineteen.

MR BROWN: How were the rest of your exam questions?
PADDINGTON: They allowed half an hour for each question. The trouble is, they didn't leave any time for the answers.

PADDINGTON: I think people were much luckier in the old days.
JONATHAN: Why is that?
PADDINGTON: They didn't have so much history to learn.

MRS BIRD: Hard work never killed anyone yet, Paddington.
PADDINGTON: I don't want to risk being the first.

MRS BIRD: I think you'd better go to bed now, Paddington. You need plenty of sleep now you've started school.

PADDINGTON: Oh, I'm not going again. The headmaster said I don't have to.

MRS BIRD: Why ever not?

PADDINGTON: They've given me my BCSE. It's like a GCSE, but specially for bears. In fact, it's the only one of its kind. I must go and write to Aunt Lucy about it...

Knock knock!
Who's there?
Paddington.
Paddington who?

Paddington Brown from Darkest Peru, and I haven't quite worked out the answer. But I hope you enjoyed reading this book as much as I enjoyed writing it.